MORTY BAYLISS

RED SEA SHARKS

IN DEPTH
ADVENTURE GUIDES

RED SEA SHARKS

Jeremy Stafford-Deitsch

Published by Trident Press Ltd

Text: © Jeremy Stafford-Deitsch, 1999

Pictures: © Jeremy Stafford-Deitsch, unless
otherwise credited.

Layout and design: © Trident Press Ltd

IN DEPTH Adventure Guides is an imprint of
Trident Press.

Series Editor: Peter Vine

General Editor: Paula Vine

Illustrations: Ian Fergusson

Typesetting and layout: Johan Hofsteenge

Cover design: Justin King

British Library Cataloguing in Publication Data.
A CIP Catalogue record for this book is available
from the British Library.

ISBNs: HB: 1-900724-28-6; PB: 1-900724-36-7

Printed in the United Arab Emirates

Trident Press Ltd

2-5 Old Bond Street

London, W1X3TB

UK

Tel: 0171 491 8770

Fax: 0171 491 8664

Email: admin@tridentpress.ie

Internet: www.tridentpress.com

IN DEPTH Adventure Guides are small, affordable guide books packed with 'must-have' information for active people pursuing a wide range of outdoor activities. The imprint title, IN DEPTH, alludes firstly to the fact that many of the books in the series will deal with underwater subjects – such as guides to sharks of different regions; and secondly to the in depth nature of the information within these small guides – all of which are written by experts in their respective fields.

IN DEPTH Adventure Guides aim to provide accurate information, based on first-hand description of wildlife, natural environments and related subjects.

CONTENTS

PART ONE: Shark Biology & Behaviour

PART TWO: Shark Identification

An emperor angelfish Pomacanthus imperator *glides down a coral wall. Despite its lack of speed, it is extremely agile and can flit into a crevice when threatened.*

INTRODUCTION

The Red Sea's sharks have been famous ever since the pioneering adventures of Hans Hass, Jacques-Yves Cousteau and Tintin. Once sleepy seaside towns on the Egyptian Red Sea coast such as Hurghada and Sharm el Sheikh have been transformed, seemingly overnight, into massive dive resorts boasting numerous hotels that cater for an ever growing influx of divers. Other divers, keen to escape the crowds and experience something of the wilderness diving of the Red Sea at its best, travel to remote areas on live-aboard boats. In the last few decades divers and sharks have met underwater increasingly often. In the vast majority of cases the diver has not been harassed or harmed by the shark and has come away thrilled by the encounter. As divers have realized that even the most powerful of sharks rarely poses a threat to them, so curiosity about these magnificent beasts has replaced fear and interest has soared.

There are few non-specialist books dealing with shark identification. Even fewer cater especially for divers. Scientists often rely on a host of esoteric details, such as tooth number and shape, vertebral count, proportion of fin height to total body length and so on, to identify similar-looking species but such details require a carcass. Some sharks are easily identified from afar, others are not. Furthermore, many of the so-called common names used to identify sharks by the layperson are confusing, contradictory, overlapping between species, or just plain wrong. Indeed all such features are embodied in the various names applied to the shark conventionally called the grey reef shark (although it is neither grey nor confined to reefs!). This species, or at least the Red Sea variety, has a black edge to the tail and a white mark

on the back edge of the apex of the first dorsal fin. Some divers call it a blacktip shark and others a whitetip. As we shall see, the situation is even more confusing as there are other sharks commonly known as whitetips and blacktips. Another name recently used for the Red Sea variety of grey reef shark was the blacktail shark: there was a debate among shark taxonomists as to whether this shark is distinct from the grey reef shark of the central Indian Ocean and Pacific. Now that that debate has subsided, grey reef shark has reinstated itself as the informed common name.

The aim of this guide is to provide a sketch of the natural history and behaviour of sharks in general and then to facilitate the identification of the sharks a Red Sea diver is most likely to encounter. The guide will be useful for identifying many of the sharks encountered on Indo-Pacific coral reefs far beyond the Red Sea: no species listed here is confined to the Red Sea and several even occur in the Atlantic.

DISCLAIMER

Sharks are potentially dangerous and unpredictable animals. While the author offers his opinion on those activities that may make encounters with sharks less dangerous, neither he, nor Trident Press, accept any responsibility whatever for the safety of those who choose to dive with sharks, regardless of whether or not they are following the author's own safety suggestions. They do so entirely at their own risk.

The range of colours from white to black on different fins of the Red Sea's variety of grey reef shark have led to confusion over both the scientific and the common name.

12

During the day, sweepers – Pempherididae *– mass in their thousands close to the coral in search of protection. During the night they move out into the water column in order to feed on plankton.*

PART ONE
SHARK BIOLOGY
& BEHAVIOUR

SHARKS AND DIVERS

Sharks belong to an ancient and extraordinary side-branch of vertebrate evolution that can be traced back some 400 million years in the fossil record. The group includes two other remarkable classes of fishes: rays and chimaeras. Rays are familiar enough to divers. Their more spectacular members include the eagle ray and the manta ray. Chimaeras, on the other hand, are small deep-water creatures that look as if they have escaped from the pages of a science fiction novel. They are rarely seen by divers.

The vast majority of the world's fishes, some 95 per cent, have a bony skeleton and are collectively termed bony fishes. The skeleton of sharks, skates and rays is composed of cartilage and they are termed cartilaginous fishes. In fact cartilaginous fishes differ from bony fishes in many other ways as well. Major differences include reproductive, developmental and excretory methods, digestive system, skeletal structure, sensory mechanisms, the composition of the skin, the lack of a swim bladder and ribs (when present) that do not protect the internal organs. Furthermore cartilaginous fishes typically have numerous gill openings on each side of the head or body (normally five), although on this last point chimaeras, like bony fishes, have only one. Indeed so different are sharks, rays and chimaeras from bony fishes in so many fundamental details that some experts wonder whether they should be called fishes at all.

Distinguishing a shark from a ray is usually simple enough. Most sharks are basically cylinder-shaped and free-swimming, while rays tend to be flattened and the majority are typically encountered lying on or swimming sluggishly just above the sea bed. However, there are varieties from both groups that are often mistaken by

The bow-mouth guitarfish is an uncommon but widespread Indo-Pacific species. The head region is covered in ridges lined with enlarged dermal denticles – in effect an external armour of teeth.

the layperson: sharks that are erroneously called rays and vice versa. Angel sharks, which are not found in the Red Sea, are flattened like rays and lie in ambush on the bottom. Guitarfishes, members of the ray group, are occasionally seen by divers and all too often erroneously called guitarsharks. In fact a good general method of distinguishing sharks from rays is to look for the gill openings: if they are on the side of the body then one is looking at a shark; if they are on the underside, it is a ray. An example of a guitarfish occasionally seen on Red Sea reefs is the bowmouth guitarfish *Rhina ancylostoma.*

Then again, there are sawfishes and sawsharks, both of which have an elongated, tooth-lined snout. Sawsharks are not recorded from the Red Sea and although sawfishes do occur, sightings by divers are rare.

GENERALIZED SHARK

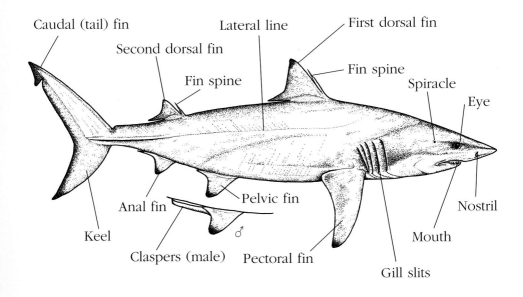

Caudal (tail) fin

Second dorsal fin

Lateral line

First dorsal fin

Fin spine

Fin spine

Spiracle

Eye

Anal fin

Pelvic fin

Nostril

Keel

Claspers (male)

Pectoral fin

Mouth

Gill slits

As more and more deep-water sharks are recorded from around the world so the species number gradually rises. At present it is slowly but surely moving towards the 400 mark. Many of these sharks are relatively small (less than 1 metre in length) and occupy depths beyond the reach of divers. However, sharks do not appear to penetrate beyond the first few thousand metres of the ocean depths. The total number of species in the Red Sea is about 40, of which perhaps 10 can be seen by divers.

The creatures of the reef have evolved different strategies to protect themselves from sharks. For example, the squirrelfish Adioryx spinifer *spends much of the day hidden under coral overhangs. A sharp, stout spine projects backwards from the gill cover. Some sharks are fairly specialized in the prey they hunt on the reef, while others – the largest predatory species – are generalists relying on a combination of speed, cunning and brute power.*

To find the sharks associated with a particular reef it is best to look in areas of current where there are soft corals and schooling fishes. Sharks tend to be found where the action is.

Sharks are the apex predators of the habitats in which they occur. The better the conditions of a particular reef – the more life it supports – the more likely there are to be sharks on it.

WHERE ARE SHARKS FOUND ON RED SEA CORAL REEFS?

If one is specifically hoping to see sharks on a coral reef then there are certainly areas on which to focus. Sharks tend to be found where the action is – which is usually where there are currents. The currents sweep plankton and nutrients across that particular part of the reef. Bony fishes often aggregate in these areas not only to feed but also to mate. The currents carry the freshly fertilized eggs out to sea to begin their planktonic development. Furthermore, the currents carry the smell of potential food, including dead or injured creatures, a considerable distance and sharks are often found milling about down current, presumably waiting for just such smells. Reef corners and promontories which are covered in soft corals, swept by currents and populated by schooling masses of jacks and barracudas – these are the places to dive in search of sharks. But working against the current requires skill, fitness and control of air consumption. The one thing to be avoided is being swept off the reef into open water: this is precisely the area where sharks can be waiting and they are likely to take you for an injured or ill reef creature if you cannot swim back to the reef.

While some sharks, such as the grey reef shark, can be encountered on both inshore and offshore reefs, others, such as the blackfin reef shark, are only likely to be observed on coastal reefs. The oceanic whitetip shark typically lives far offshore although it does appear alongside the walls of open-water reefs in the Red Sea, such as The Brothers. Occasionally, oceanic whitetips also appear off coastal reefs that plunge into deep water.

DO DIFFERENT TYPES OF SHARK PREFER DIFFERENT TYPES OF REEF?

19

Right: The oceanic whitetip is a bold wanderer of the tropical oceans of the world. It occasionally puts in a majestic appearance on coral reefs that drop into deep water. Note the juvenile pilotfish Naucrates ductor *riding the pressure wave in front of the snout of this shark.*

Some species, such as the tiger shark, usually swim in deep water during the day and come into shallower water at night. The tiger shark is another example of a shark that can occur just about anywhere, from the shallowest inshore to the deepest offshore waters.

Above: The southern point of Sha'ab Rumi Reef in the Sudanese Red Sea is famous for its aggregations of grey reef sharks. The swollen bellies of these females show that they are all pregnant. They may synchronize giving birth and perhaps the pups school in deep water off the reef.

Little is known about the movement patterns of sharks within the Red Sea. A particular reef can be swarming with them on one day and deserted the next. Another can seem to have a fairly stable population of sharks throughout the year.

One species may suddenly move in on a reef for a few days and then vanish never to be seen there again. A school of hammerheads may be in evidence on a reef for a few dives and then not appear again for weeks or months. We do not know why hammerheads school, let alone where they go in their schools.

How likely is a diver to see a shark on a Red Sea reef?

It is possible to see sharks on just about any healthy reef. The whitetip reef shark is perhaps the one most commonly seen on coastal reefs, while certain reefs, for example open-water reefs in the Egyptian Red Sea such as the Brothers, Daedalus and Rocky Island, as well as offshore reefs in the Sudan, can be virtually guaranteed to provide sightings of other types as well.

Areas that are very heavily dived can apparently lose their sharks, although it may be that the sharks now keep their distance. Similarly, a rarely dived reef can give the impression that it is infested with sharks, as any sharks which are in the area may become curious and swim up to investigate the diver. Moreover, on a reef where others have regularly fed the sharks, they may come in very close in the hope that you are going to feed them.

Are the sharks seen on reefs confined to reefs?

Some species, such as the variegated shark and the whitetip reef shark, are virtually confined to the coral reef ecosystem; many species are not. It is often assumed that because divers tend to see a particular species of shark in a particular setting that that is the natural (and only) habitat of that species. For example, the grey reef shark is typically encountered on coral reefs, but this may be due to the fact that divers tend to dive coral reefs in the tropics more than other areas. I have occasionally encountered grey reef sharks in deep water far from any reef, sometimes associated with other creatures such as marine mammals or sailfishes. Again,

A shark can make a close approach for a variety of reasons, the two most obvious being aggression and curiosity. On reefs where the sharks are often fed, they will quickly learn to associate boats and divers with feeding and approach closely in the hope that they are being brought food. A diver who ventures to such a reef unknowingly can mistake the sharks' expectations for aggression.

there may be periods when grey reef sharks move away from reefs en masse for unknown reasons. A few years ago I was diving some coral reefs in New Guinea. I was surprised, after several days, not to have seen any grey reef sharks on reefs where I would normally expect to

Swimming with bottlenose dolphins can be dangerous: sharks in the vicinity often react aggressively to the human intruder. The over-excited behaviour of the dolphins and the clumsy movements of the human can make the sharks target the person, mistaking him or her for an injured marine mammal.

see them. One morning a huge school of bottlenose dolphins swam past the boat in deep water just beyond the reef we were diving. I snorkelled over to try to photograph them and they swam off. But they were immediately replaced by about 50 sharks swirling aggressively around me that had obviously been swimming just behind and below the dolphins. There were about 25 silky sharks, 25 grey reef sharks, one silvertip – and one frightened snorkeller!

The appearance of sharks on a particular reef may be due to the activities of the creatures on the reef – perhaps the formation of mating schools of bony fishes that are easy to feed on. Or it may be that the sharks aggregate to mate or give birth. Or the answer may be something very different. No one really knows.

Unlike bony fishes, sharks lack a swim bladder – a gas-filled bladder for buoyancy control. This has given rise to the myth that sharks, being heavier than water, must swim or sink. A sealed gas-filled bladder is not a good idea for an animal that moves rapidly up and down in the water column (as all divers know). In fact, most sharks have a large liver in which they store oils that are lighter than sea water and this is an efficient means of buoyancy control, independent of depth. Furthermore, the fin and head shape of a free-swimming shark naturally impart upward lift to minimize the effort needed to swim without sinking. Some species of shark intentionally swallow air to make themselves lighter. The sand tiger shark does this and can hover just above the bottom. One diver told me of a scalloped hammerhead shark which swam up towards him from the depths, belching air as it approached.

IS A SHARK DOOMED TO SWIM OR SINK?

Without such tricks, the tendency of a shark to sink is considerable. I remember trying to lift a dead 3 metre hammerhead shark off the bottom in the Bahamas. It required a buoyancy compensator filled with air and a great deal of finning.

There is a myth that sharks must swim constantly to pass water over the gills, in order to avoid suffocating. In fact, many species are quite capable of lying on the bottom and pumping water over the gills. Indeed the whitetip reef shark is largely nocturnal and is often seen during the day resting on the bottom. Most sharks have the mouth located on the underside of the head and one of the problems with lying on a sandy substrate is that sand particles can be taken in by the mouth and interfere with the delicate blood vessels of the gills. For this reason sharks that are adapted to spending a great deal of time

CAN SHARKS REST ON THE BOTTOM?

25

on the seabed usually have an alternative opening for taking in water, an orifice behind each eye called the spiracle, which minimizes the intake of sand.

The whitetip reef shark is often encountered during the day lying on the bottom. Many sharks are perfectly capable of resting on the sea floor for hours at a time.

SENSORY MECHANISMS

Sharks have a range of very sophisticated sensory mechanisms for locating prey. The most long-range is probably what we would call sound – the detection of vibrations passing through the water. Scientists have shown that sharks are attracted over distances of several kilometres to artificial low frequency sound pulses that correspond to the sounds produced by a struggling fish. Not only do sharks have ears (though without conspicuous external parts), but they also have a pressure-sensitive lateral line extending down each side of the body which detects water-borne vibrations.

The head of a grey reef shark showing the eye, mouth, snout and nostril. The ampullae of Lorenzini – sensory pores that detect electrical fields – are visible around the eye.

The very large olfactory centres in the brain of a shark attest to the importance of smell for locating food. Indeed experiments in aquaria show that sharks can smell the most minute concentrations of dissolved food. The Atlantic lemon shark can detect 1 part of tuna extract in 25 million parts of water, while the grey reef shark is claimed to be able to detect 1 part of tuna extract in an almost unbelievable 10 billion parts of water. Little wonder that sharks are often referred to as swimming noses.

The eyes of sharks are designed to see well in low light situations and many species are capable of colour vision as well. The presence of a tapetum layer in the eye of many species allows for good nocturnal vision; the limited available light that enters the eye is amplified back. It is little comfort to a diver on a night dive to know that any shark concealed in the blackness can doubtlessly see him. Some sharks, such as the grey reef and silvertip shark, have a protective third eyelid called the nictitating membrane, that closes to protect the eye when the shark is biting something.

The snout of a shark is peppered with small jelly-filled pores called the ampullae of Lorenzini. These are known to be capable of detecting the tiny electrical fields induced by living creatures. An animal such as a flatfish that buries itself in the sand will, therefore, not be concealed from a hunting shark that passes close by. It is even suspected that sharks can use this sense to detect the earth's own magnetic field and hence navigate.

REPRODUCTION AND DEVELOPMENT

A dispassionate consideration of the sensory apparatus of a shark suggests that one is dealing with an immensely sophisticated animal – certainly not the primitive eating machine that the popular press would have us believe. This view is more than confirmed when one considers its reproductive processes. Bony fishes produce massive numbers of eggs and sperm, and fertilization occurs outside the body. When one compares the quantity of raw materials used with the number of mature survivors of the next generation, this can be seen to be a very wasteful process, although with one vital advantage: populations of bony fishes can fluctuate considerably and bounce back from local disasters. Sharks, however, have employed a different strategy for hundreds of millions of years, a strategy that has proved successful up until only the last few decades. Fertilization is internal. Indeed a mature male shark can easily be identified underwater by the presence of claspers – intromittent organs – extending backwards from between the pelvic fins.

The pair of claspers extending backwards from between the pelvic fins of this whitetip reef shark identify it as a mature male.

Courtship in sharks has occasionally been witnessed in the wild. The female probably produces pheromones (scent signals) to attract the male; divers have on various occasions seen a female shark with several males following closely behind – presumably having been attracted to the female as a precursor to mating. In many species the male will take hold of the female with his teeth before or during mating and the gashes and scars of such encounters are commonplace on mature female sharks. (In some species the female actually has thicker skin than the male.)

Mature female sharks often have numerous scars and gashes presumably from mating. Note the scars to the body and damage to the first dorsal fin of this female grey reef shark.

The variegated shark is an egg-laying (oviparous) shark commonly seen on certain Red Sea reefs.

Once fertilization has occurred there are three basic methods of development. The most primitive is termed ovipary: the developing young is expelled from the mother's body in a yolk-filled egg case. (The egg case usually has tendrils of some sort to attach it to the seabed or seaweed. Or it may be corkscrew-shaped permitting it to be anchored in the sand or wedged into a gully.) Once the pup has exhausted its supply of yolk it must struggle out of the egg case and face the risks of the open sea. The variegated shark is oviparous.

Ovovivipary is a considerable advance on ovipary. In this method the pup develops within the relative safety of the mother's uterus. Each pup has a yolk sac attached to it for nourishment. In some species unfertilized eggs are also devoured by the young, while in a few species the smaller pups are devoured by the larger – a technique termed intra-uterine cannibalism. Ovovivipary is the most common developmental mechanism in sharks and the shortfin mako – a large, swift, offshore shark that occurs in the Red Sea but is rarely if ever spotted by divers – is an ovoviviparous intra-uterine cannibal. The pelagic thresher is an egg-eating (oophagous) ovoviviparous shark occasionally seen off deep-water reefs in the Red Sea.

The most advanced method of development in sharks is termed vivipary. This process parallels that of mammals in that a placental connection is established between the pup and the mother – although sharks invented this method long before mammals were even a twinkle in Mother Nature's eye. The majority of the sharks a diver is likely to encounter on the reefs of the Red Sea are viviparous. Indeed all the sharks commonly referred to as grey or requiem sharks (the family Carcharhinidae) are viviparous, with the sole exception of the tiger shark which is ovoviviparous. The grey reef shark, the silky, the oceanic whitetip and all the other members of the genus Carcharhinus are viviparous. Hammerheads – of which the scalloped hammerhead is the common Red Sea example – are also viviparous. This is hardly surprising when one realizes that hammerheads are the most recently evolved of sharks, appearing only a few tens of millions of years ago. They are thought to have evolved from requiem sharks.

The shortfin mako Isurus oxyrinchus *is perhaps the swiftest of all sharks. It has a worldwide distribution in tropical and temperate waters and has been implicated in an attack on a human in the Red Sea. Fortunately, the shortfin mako is an open-water shark that usually stays away from coral reefs frequented by divers.*

SHARKS AND THEIR ESCORTS

It is not unusual to see suckerfishes either attached to, or swimming next to, a shark. The upper surface of the head is flattened into a disc that can be used to attach it to the host. The suckerfish then receives a free ride. Some species will attach to a variety of hosts while others are fairly specific in their requirements.

Open-water sharks are often accompanied by pilotfishes, although the myth that they guide the shark to prey has long been discarded. The number of pilotfishes accompanying a shark can vary considerably.

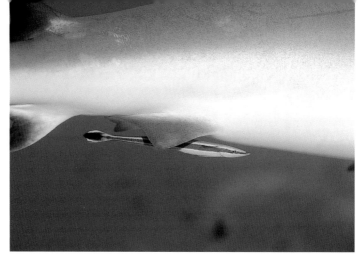

A suckerfish Echeneis naucrates *swims between the pelvic fins of a grey reef shark. The suction-pad on the head allows the suckerfish to attach for a free ride.*

Juvenile pilotfishes are occasionally to be seen riding the pressure wave immediately in front of the snout of a variety of sharks such as the silky, silvertip and oceanic whitetip. However, adult pilotfishes appear to favour the oceanic whitetip and in the Red Sea several dozen mature fishes often accompany each oceanic whitetip shark.

Brown remoras Remora remora *have attached themselves between the paired fins of this oceanic whitetip shark. It is also escorted by pilotfishes* Naucrates ductor.

CONSERVATION

Sharks produce only a few pups at a time – miniature versions of the adult. Each pup has a reasonable chance of surviving into adulthood provided that the challenges under which the species established itself remain constant. An advantage of this process is that once established the animal in question can exist at saturation level – the maximum number of individuals that the environment can carry. A crucial disadvantage – as we are about to see – is that if the pressures facing the animal in question increase dramatically, then the animal may not be capable of bouncing back and re-establishing itself. For example, it has been calculated that if more than 5 per cent of a population of sharks is removed annually from a given area, the entire population will soon collapse. Work has been done on the Atlantic lemon shark that vividly demonstrates this vulnerability. It can take a female lemon shark 15 years to reach sexual maturity. Pregnancy lasts a year and the female will not mate again for another year after the birth of her pups. Typically 8 – 12 pups are born each alternate year. The mortality of these pups in the first year is about 50 per cent. Only 1 to 3 pups are likely to survive into the third year – and there are another 12 years to go before the female reaches sexual maturity (the male can mature sooner). If the number of sharks being killed increases rapidly then the ability of surviving sharks to fill the gaps collapses.

Traditionally, sharks faced predation from only a few sources. The first is from larger sharks. For example the bull shark (probably absent from the Red Sea) and tiger shark are known to feed on smaller sharks. Another predatory threat to sharks is the killer whale. But in the last few decades an enormous new threat has appeared.

Juvenile scalloped hammerheads schooling in the Sudanese Red Sea. The tendency of many shark species to form aggregations – which are often sexually segregated – makes them especially vulnerable to overfishing. The schooling hammerheads I have occasionally observed in the Red Sea have invariably been female.

The crisis facing the world's shark populations is due to unregulated commercial fishing. It is estimated that well over 100 million sharks are caught annually by commercial fishing fleets and, as we have seen, sharks simply do not have the reproductive capacity to survive this level of slaughter. Furthermore, many species are sexually segregated for much of their lives, which means that catching all the sharks in an area can eradicate one sex.

Some sharks are caught for their flesh – for example the shortfin mako tastes as good as any quality game fish – others for their liver oils or skin. Sharks are even being caught to provide cartilage for pseudo-scientific miracle cures for cancer that do not work. Sports fishermen like

A diver observes a silky shark in the Sudanese Red Sea.

to demonstrate their heroism by catching sharks. There is a considerable trophy industry for shark parts: jaws to be hung in vulgar display and teeth to be worn in vulgar jewellery. Huge numbers of sharks die because they are accidentally caught by commercial fishing fleets targeting other creatures such as swordfishes. However, the greatest crisis facing the world's sharks is due to the international

Sharks should be understood as intrinsic components of the ecosystems in which they occur. Removal of the apex predators is likely to have disastrous effects on the stability of the ecosystem as a whole.

fin trade. The fins are used to produce shark's fin soup, an oriental delicacy for which supply has never matched demand. With the vast increase in oriental restaurants the world over, the demand has reached insatiable proportions. A fisherman can catch a shark, slice off the valuable fins and throw the body – dead or alive – back into the sea. The fins are light and easily stored in some out of the way part of the boat while the hold is filled with more commercially valuable fishes such as tuna or swordfish. Indeed much of the international trade in shark fins is now run by gangsters. Traders approach fishermen the world over and offer good prices for shark fins. Dealers in the Far East who used to trade in animal parts such as rhino horn, elephant ivory and bear gall-bladders have simply side-stepped the international outcry that such imports have occasioned and switched instead to the decimation of sharks for their fins. Few people care about protecting sharks, so in the Red Sea and through-out the Arabian region, uncounted numbers of sharks are being removed from the marine environment. Yemeni fishing fleets are among the worst culprits, although the trade is probably now ubiquitous, both in geographical scope and also the nationality of fishermen involved. A few summers ago Yemeni fishing boats poached countless numbers of sharks from Sudanese and southern Egyptian reefs. Stories of devastated shark populations and overnight millionaires filter out of other regions as well. The sharks off the Somali coast are rumoured to be all but gone. The effect of the removal of sharks from the marine environment is incalculable. It can only disrupt the ecosystems of which sharks are not only a spectacular but an integral component.

Scuba divers who have the opportunity to dive with sharks and see these daunting predators in their natural state surely have a moral obligation to speak up for and support their protection. Certainly the sharks seen by tourist divers on a coral reef – sharks that may specif-ically attract the divers to that reef – are vastly more valuable to the local economy than the handful of dollars a fisherman might obtain for their fins. While it is obvious

As divers learn that sharks generally pose little threat to humans so interest in diving with, and filming, these magnificent animals has soared.

to anyone involved in the Red Sea diving industry that the sharks are an essential and dramatic constituent of the industry, that attitude hardly reaches beyond those involved in diving tourism. A problem the world over is that those reefs to which divers flock specifically to observe sharks, are tempting for fishermen in search of yet more targets. Some fishermen think that they are making the seas safer and doing divers a favour by catching precisely the sharks the divers hope to see! It makes little sense to attempt to protect coral reefs that are in good enough condition to sustain sharks while simultaneously allowing fishermen to remove them. Either the ecosystem deserves protection *in toto* or it does not.

If you are interested in more detailed information on shark identification, biology and conservation, visit The Shark Trust's website at:

http://ds.dial.pipex.com/sharktrust

The great white shark is arguably the most dangerous of all species, although it is nowhere very common and always rare in the tropics. There are one or two claims of white sharks captured in the Red Sea in past centuries but it may be that the scientific name was being incorrectly applied to other species (a common problem then). The great white has been recorded off Kuwait, the Seychelles and Mauritius and Hans Hass claims to have been molested by one on Sanganeb Reef in the Sudanese Red Sea, so it is possible that there are one or two in the Red Sea. But one would have to be the luckiest – or unluckiest – of divers to encounter a great white.

There may be great white sharks in the Red Sea. They are certainly present in the Mediterranean and also in neighbouring Indian Ocean waters. The rich supply of dolphins in the Red Sea would provide a suitable food source – dolphins are an invaluable component of the Mediterranean white shark's diet. This white shark was photographed off southern Australia.

DIVING WITH SHARKS

It used to be thought that the appearance of a shark spelled doom for a diver. Old dive books used to suggest that the only sensible thing to do if a shark appeared was to leave the water. No mention was made of the conditions under which the shark put in its appearance, its species, its behaviour or the time of day. We now know that sharks in general pose little threat. Again and again divers encounter sharks underwater and the experience is usually safe and exhilarating. I have dived with sharks many hundreds of times and only on half a dozen occasions have I felt myself to have been in any danger. Moreover, on those occasions when I have been in danger, the wisdom of hindsight has usually made it clear why. At the end of this chapter, therefore, I offer advice derived from my own experiences.

DANGER AND DIET

Different species of shark eat different things – a shark that specializes in eating shellfish and lobsters, such as the tawny shark, has teeth designed for crushing through shells. Such an animal is no more likely to try to eat a human than is a goldfish. Nevertheless, it can bite defensively if threatened – and to considerably more effect than a goldfish. Defensive biting is a natural response by many animals and sharks are no exception. The fact that a shark has no intention of eating you does not mean that it will not bite.

WARNING SIGNS

The Indo-Pacific variety of the grey reef shark will, on occasion, warn a diver who is pestering or following it that it is about to launch an attack. The pectoral fins are

The variety of grey reef shark encountered on Red Sea coral reefs is, occasionally, capable of unprovoked and unpredictable acts of aggression towards a diver or snorkeller. However, it normally shows no interest in human beings.

lowered, the snout lifted and the body contorted into an 's' shape. The shark may swim in a tight figure of eight pattern or stop swimming altogether before launching its attack (although it might also flee without attacking). It is not clear whether the grey reef shark of the Red Sea performs such a threat display but obviously any shark that is swimming erratically must not be followed. Sometimes the firing of an underwater camera can be the trigger that launches an attack, so, if a shark is swimming erratically do *not* try to photograph it.

45

This oceanic whitetip is opening and shutting its mouth and shaking its head vigorously from side to side. Such behaviour is clearly a warning not to approach any closer.

Other sharks perform what are probably also threat displays, and indeed such displays may be widespread (and not even limited to sharks) underwater; the problem is that we do not know the signals. I have seen an oceanic whitetip rapidly open and shut its mouth and shake its head from side to side when I blocked its path, which was presumably a warning to let it pass.

ATTACKING TO FEED

The behaviour described above is defensive in origin. Much more dangerous, however, are attacks launched by sharks that are attempting to devour the victim. Generally speaking such attacks are most likely from sharks that are capable of biting chunks out of an animal too large to swallow whole. Such sharks tend to be large and generalist feeders – feeding on a wide variety of prey items. Their teeth are usually more or less triangular in shape and serrated. The teeth of a shark that catches small fishes and swallows them whole are usually thin and pointed, designed for impaling prey which is then gulped intact.

In the inshore waters of the tropics, the most dangerous common shark (although it is rarely seen by divers) is probably the tiger shark, which is indeed present in the Red Sea. Other potentially dangerous sharks of tropical waters include the oceanic whitetip (also present), the bull shark (very rare or absent from the Red Sea) and other requiem sharks which have attained a good size.

ATTACKS ON DIVERS

Thankfully attacks on divers are extremely rare. A diver underwater usually attracts less interest from a shark than a snorkeller or a swimmer. Some divers have the curious habit of behaving cautiously when diving where large sharks are likely to be encountered, but then, having finished their dive, of jumping into the sea and splashing and swimming on the surface as if such sharks no longer existed! I have often seen tourist divers do this on offshore reefs and even go for a swim in open water:

Sharks encountered in open water – and especially sharks adapted to living in open water – can behave very differently from reef sharks. The oceanic whitetip will fearlessly approach and even bump into an object on the surface to investigate it as a potential meal.

Open water sharks encountered on coral reefs can be expected to be either curious or aggressive. This 2.5 metre silky shark made several rapid, close approaches to me on Sha'ab Rumi reef.

both activities invite trouble. If you have to go for a swim in such areas then put on mask, fins and snorkel, enter the water quietly, swim calmly on the surface, constantly survey in all directions – and stay close to the boat. Do not jump in and thrash about, giving off the erratic signals of an injured animal.

Most sharks seen on a dive will ignore the diver or move away. A few will approach for a close look and then keep their distance. Any shark that repeatedly comes close – or worse still, starts bumping in to you – is obviously investigating you as a potential meal.

Such approaches are common from open-water sharks such as the oceanic whitetip and the silky. Silvertips will also approach in this manner. Any attack from such a shark is likely to come after several minutes (or even hours) of increasingly aggressive approaches, and one must always have the ability to leave the water promptly. While open-water species are often far more aggressive than those on reefs, reef sharks, such as the grey reef shark, can become aggressive when encountered in open water. And open-water sharks encountered on coral reefs can behave very differently from the typical sharks of the reef. I remember a particular silky shark that turned up at Sha'ab Rumi Reef in the Sudanese Red Sea and delighted in harassing divers wherever they chose to dive. It would turn up after a few minutes, day or night, and make increasingly aggressive passes until the dive was aborted.

A general rule is to be able to identify any shark immediately it appears, as this may well help to assess how much of a threat it is likely to pose.

TIME OF DAY

Many sharks are crepuscular in their feeding patterns – they feed at dawn and dusk unless other opportunities arise. There is thus no question that diving early in the morning or late in the afternoon greatly increases the risk of attack. Along with other divers, I have on occasion been harassed and chased by grey reef sharks at dusk that were timid and kept their distance during the day. Other larger sharks such as the oceanic whitetip and silky are to be considered especially dangerous during these times and entering the water with them then is not advised.

Strange as it may seem it is not always the larger sharks that pose the greatest risk. Occasionally, it is the youngsters that show a lack of respect while the grand adults circle timidly in the distance. Some biologists think that the larger adults have attained their size through a careful combination of caution and aggression, while among the smaller sharks there is a sizeable proportion that will not reach adulthood, precisely because of excessive risk-taking in search of a meal. On the other hand, although I can recall several occasions when it was smaller sharks that posed a threat, there have been others when it was the larger sharks that were alarmingly bold.

FEEDING SHARKS

It has become common practice for divers around the world to feed reef sharks in order to bring them in close enough to be filmed or photographed. Indeed, this is often the only reliable way of taking pictures of them (most of the pictures in this book required offering food to the sharks to bring them in close). There is a debate now raging about whether shark feeding should ever be allowed. In some parts of the world shark feeding has degenerated into a circus and unnaturally large numbers of sharks have come to depend on being fed. They have also lost all fear of divers with the result that divers have been bitten. Eventually a fatality may result.

If you wish to attend a shark feed then make sure the following rules are enforced:

- The bait (dead fish) should be easily accessible to the sharks: some divers wrap the food up with wire trace or chain which will damage a shark's mouth when it tries to get the food. (Live fish should never be speared in front of sharks. They will become

Grey reef sharks are usually wary of divers and getting close enough to obtain a good picture is almost impossible without using dead fish as bait to bring them in.

dangerously aggressive – and spearfishing is illegal on many reefs.)

- Divers should position themselves up current from the food source and at least 3 metres away. They should sit calmly and not swim towards the sharks (which are often hesitant to feed anyway).
- Only whitetip reef sharks and grey reef sharks should be fed. Feeding of other species such as the tiger, silky and oceanic whitetip should not be attempted. These large, bold sharks are perfectly capable of biting the hand that feeds them. If such a shark appears during a feed it is sensible to retreat. Scalloped hammerheads are usually very timid and rarely come in to feed.

By hiding dead fish in an appropriate place on a reef, the local sharks can be enticed to swim into the most photogenic position. However, being so close to the hidden bait makes such activity potentially dangerous.

The grey reef sharks of the Red Sea can normally be fed in relative safety, although one does occasionally encounter an aggressive one. It is not unknown to have one's underwater strobe bumped or bitten when it is recycling – the high-pitched whine seems to attract sharks. Furthermore, they can take an alarming interest in brightly coloured fins (and also the clear plastic variety) and colourful diving equipment.

SHARKS AND MARINE MAMMALS

Sharks often accompany marine mammals in open water, so swimming in open water with marine mammals is something of a risk. I have seen silky, grey reef, oceanic whitetip, silvertip and Galapagos sharks swimming with shortfin pilot whales, false killer whales and bottlenose dolphins. Anyone tempted to jump into the water with marine mammals should be alert to the very real possibility that sharks will be accompanying them. Such sharks can treat intruding humans with considerable aggression – swimming rapidly up to them and bumping in to them. (If this happens then you will not need to be advised to leave the water – you will already have left!) It may be that the sharks mistake a snorkeller for an injured marine mammal and therefore regard him or her as an easy meal. Similarly, any marine mammals that swim past a reef can become over-excited by divers or snorkellers joining them, and the reef sharks may be attracted in accordingly.

On the 23rd of July, 1996, Martin Richardson, a novice diver, was bitten by sharks off Marsa Bareka, Sharm el Sheikh. He had been swimming with bottlenose dolphins when attacked. Several of the dolphins surrounded him and by beating their flukes and fins on the surface of the water, apparently prevented further attack. He was subsequently rescued and, thanks to a combination of quick medical attention and evacuation, survived. The attack culminated after several high-risk details came together. Indeed, with the wisdom of hindsight, the attack appears to have been virtually inevitable.

The victim and two others went swimming (apparently without mask/fins/snorkel) in deep water with bottlenose dolphins. It was late afternoon – a time when many sharks start hunting/feeding. Sharks often accompany or hunt dolphins. By swimming, rather than snorkelling, the humans would have been giving off chaotic vibrations that any nearby sharks would have immediately associated with injured marine mammals. (The dolphins would have been echo-locating and swimming excitedly as well – increasing the underwater atmosphere of chaos and confusion.) Furthermore, by not wearing masks, the swimmers would not have seen any sharks around them (the sharks might well have made preliminary close approaches – if the swimmers had worn masks they might have seen the sharks and perhaps had the opportunity to get out of the water). Martin Richardson was attacked after the other two swimmers had left the water. Sharks typically target a person away from a group, or a solitary individual. The surgeon who tended the victim's wounds has said that, judging from the different size of the bites, at least two sharks were involved. The largest bite had a diameter of 46 cms – which, suggests a shark of not inconsiderable size, perhaps 4 metres or more in length. The most likely candidate would be a tiger shark (commonly seen in Marsa Bareka before the area was closed off to divers

Several species of shark are known to accompany a variety of marine mammals, although the explanation for this behaviour is not known. Here, oceanic whitetips accompany shortfin pilot whales Globicephala macrorhynchus *in Hawaiian waters.*

by the military). The fact that the victim survived bites from a shark of this size shows that the shark was merely inflicting tentative, exploratory bites.

WHEN THINGS GO WRONG

The difference between a safe shark encounter and a dangerous one can depend on subtle variations in the conditions, or unfamiliarity with the sharks in question. In the summer of 1995 divers had been reporting exciting but unthreatening encounters with several silky sharks off the point of Sha'ab Rumi Reef in the Sudan.

Open-water sharks can become especially dangerous in the late afternoon. Here at Sha'ab Rumi Reef in Sudan two silky sharks swim rapidly towards me. Despite several kicks to the snout of the sharks they do not retreat but continue to swirl frantically around me. I swim back over the reef flat, snapping pictures in retreat. The silkies follow fearlessly. The silkies, undeterred by numerous kicks to their head and an occasional thump with my camera, continue their aggressive investigation over the reef flat. Luckily, the operator of the inflatable boat saw my frantic signals and returned to fetch me.

The silkies would turn up in the afternoon and circle the divers but do no more. When we dived the reef they arrived at the end of the dive and performed to order. I decided to change camera and re-entered the water about 10 minutes later to photograph them. By now it was late afternoon. As I entered the water (to snorkel) several bottlenose dolphins swam past the point. I knew it was possible that the sharks would mistake me for an injured dolphin and decided to stay against the reef wall in case I needed to swim on top of it. However, even as I entered the water two of the silkies aggressively confronted me and swam rapidly back and forth right next to me without retreating. I kicked them with my fins but this made no difference. I swam back over the reef crest and they followed, each apparently mesmerized by my frantically beating fins. Several more kicks to their heads proved ineffectual, as did several clunks with my camera. Luckily I managed to attract the operator of the inflatable boat who came to the edge of the reef and the silkies retreated just enough to allow me to get back into the boat . . .

I had broken several of my own safety rules and was lucky to get away with it. I was, in effect, snorkelling with marine mammals in the presence of open-water sharks and, worse still, it was late afternoon, when they tend to begin feeding. Furthermore I was alone – a good way to get interesting photographs because the sharks will come in closer, but they only come closer because they see you more as a victim than a threat.

SAFETY TIPS

It should be remembered that most sharks normally pose little threat to divers only because they are unfamiliar with them and their instincts warn them to treat anything unfamiliar with respect. If the large predatory sharks knew just how vulnerable a diver is, then things would be very different. All sharks are potentially dangerous and divers interacting with sharks should never become complacent. The following is a list garnered from my own experiences that should minimize, but cannot eradicate, the risk of diving with sharks:

- Never swim erratically.
- Stay in a group.
- Do not wear brightly coloured diving equipment when diving with sharks. Yellow is thought to be particularly bad; it has been called 'yum-yum' yellow by biologists investigating the colour preferences of sharks.
- Avoid swimming with sharks at dawn and dusk.
- Be able to identify the species you see so as to make a preliminary estimate of the threat it is likely to pose.
- Be aware when swimming with marine mammals that if sharks are present they can be aggressive. If sharks do appear, do not thrash about but rather swim calmly and leave the water. Always wear mask, fins and snorkel and preferably a wetsuit when swimming with marine mammals. The mask will allow you to see any sharks. Fins and snorkel will allow you to swim relatively calmly and efficiently. The wetsuit will offer protection should a curious shark bump into you. Never free-swim with marine mammals where there is the possibility of encountering sharks.
- Leave shark feeding to experienced dive masters.

- Always carry a fluorescent orange safety flag or tube: if you are swept off a reef into deep water you may need to be collected quickly.
- Always swim back to the reef wall at the end of a dive and wait to be collected there.
- Never swim so far from the reef that you cannot quickly return to it. Do not allow yourself to be swept away from the reef into open water.
- Never snorkel or dive in open water without a boat close at hand for a rapid exit.
- Never attempt to follow or photograph a shark that appears to be swimming strangely.
- If during a shark feed the sharks seem especially interested in your underwater flashgun, turn it off.
- Do not hesitate to abort a dive if the sharks are swimming rapidly or showing an interest in you.
- If a large shark such as a tiger shark appears and then vanishes, keep a good look out for it as it may return.
- Never allow the excitement of diving with sharks to cloud your common sense about when unacceptable risks are being taken: think things through.

Safety cannot be guaranteed when diving with sharks. These guidelines are not infallible as sharks are wild and unpredictable animals. Neither the author nor the publisher assume any responsibility whatever for anyone choosing to dive, swim or snorkel with sharks. They do so entirely at their own risk.

Despite the seeming tranquility of this scene, the larger of this pair of grey reef sharks at Sanganeb Reef was in fact aggressive and difficult to work with. Individual sharks within a species can behave quite differently to each other.

PART TWO
SHARK IDENTIFICATION

The sharks in this section are grouped according to distinct characteristics that the diver should be able to recognize:

Sharks with conspicuous fin markings.

Sharks with conspicuous body markings.

Sharks without conspicuous fin or body markings.

Where several similar species appear within a sub-division, the more common (and therefore more likely identification) appears earlier.

The diagrams give accurate taxonomic information about the various species. The photographic section includes photographs of all the species listed herein.

The bar after a shark's name identifies the danger it is likely to pose to a human, with more red indicating more danger.

BLACKFIN REEF SHARK
Carcharhinus melanopterus

IDENTIFICATION: The first dorsal fin and lower lobe of the tail fin have large black markings. Other fins can be black-tipped. The body is pale.

DISTRIBUTION: Found from the eastern Mediterranean (having entered via the Suez Canal) to the central Pacific.

SIZE: Typically less than 1.5 metres; maximum about 1.8 metres.

HABITAT: Coastal reefs and lagoons; aggregations of juveniles can be encountered in sheltered bays – presumably pupping areas.

DIET: Feeds on a wide range of fishes, cephalopods and crustaceans.

COMMENTS: A timid inshore shark that is usually difficult to approach underwater. It can be seen feeding on reef flats in the evening.

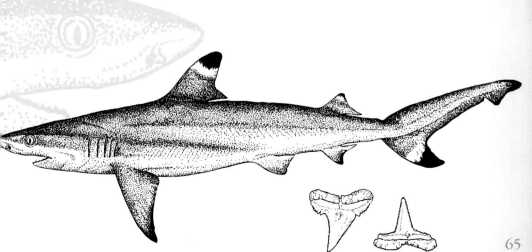

BLACKTIP REEF SHARK
Carcharhinus limbatus

IDENTIFICATION: There are pronounced black markings on the edges of the fins. The amount of black on the first dorsal fin of the blacktip is considerably less than in the blackfin reef shark. The blacktip has a pale body and a relatively long and pointed snout and the back rises noticeably to the first dorsal fin.

DISTRIBUTION: Occurs in the Mediterranean and in tropical and sub-tropical waters worldwide.

SIZE: Attains about 2.5 metres, although most are considerably smaller.

HABITAT: The blacktip is occasionally found in relatively shallow inshore waters where it occurs in a range of habitats. It is known to school, and can also be encountered offshore.

DIET: Feeds on a wide variety of bony fishes as well as an occasional cephalopod and crustacean.

COMMENTS: This is a very swift, active and excitable shark. If seen by a diver it is likely to be moving rapidly in the opposite direction.

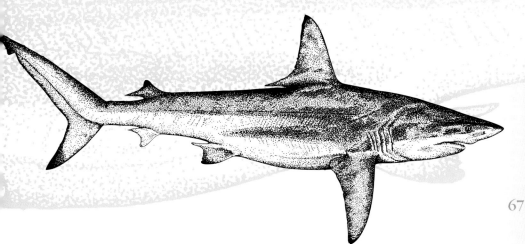

WHITETIP REEF SHARK
Triaenodon obesus

IDENTIFICATION: The apex of the first dorsal fin and the upper lobe of the tail fin normally have white markings. There can be white markings on the apex of the second dorsal fin and on the lower lobe of the tail fin. The body is thin and sometimes has dark spots on it. The second dorsal fin is relatively large while the pectoral fins are short. The snout is blunt and short.

DISTRIBUTION: Common on shallow reefs throughout the Indo-Pacific from the Red Sea to Central America.

SIZE: Maximum size may be over 2 metres but the vast majority are less than 1.5 metres in length.

HABITAT: The most commonly seen shark on inshore Red Sea reefs, although it also occurs on offshore reefs. It favours shallow parts of the reef where it swims just above the bottom. It rarely ventures into open water away from the reef.

DIET: The whitetip is a nocturnal feeder and specializes in extracting sleeping fishes from their resting place. It will also take octopuses and crustaceans.

COMMENTS: During the day it is not unusual to see whitetips at rest on the bottom or in caves and crevices. They will sometimes follow a diver along a reef (at a respectful distance) and then move off when seen.

SILVERTIP SHARK
Carcharhinus albimarginatus

IDENTIFICATION: The silvertip shark is easily recognized by the conspicuous white markings on the tips of the first dorsal fin, the pectorals and the upper and lower lobes of the caudal fin. These markings run along the rear edges of the fins in a thin line. The pelvic, anal and second dorsal fin can also have a thin white posterior edge. The silvertip is a magnificently proportioned and elegantly coloured shark. It is a swift and powerful predator.

DISTRIBUTION: A common warm-water shark of the Indo-Pacific.

SIZE: Certainly to 3 metres and there are unconfirmed reports of considerably larger specimens.

HABITAT: Usually encountered in deep water off open water reefs. It is also found in open water far from land.

DIET: The silvertip feeds on a wide range of bony fishes. Larger individuals (over 2.5 metres) can become heavily scarred. At this size they probably become more sluggish and supplement their diet by feeding on animals of the reef floor such as stingrays. Scarring is presumably from wounds from stingray barbs and collisions with coral.

COMMENTS: The silvertip is a fairly common shark of offshore Red Sea reefs. It will often make a close initial approach to investigate a diver and can be aggressive.

70

OCEANIC WHITETIP SHARK
Carcharhinus longimanus

IDENTIFICATION:	The oceanic whitetip is readily identified by the unmistakable combination of fin shape and coloration. The first dorsal fin is very large and rounded and the pectoral fins are very long. The body is a pale brown which gives way, via a blotchy intermediate area, to the white underside. Blotchy white markings occur on the first dorsal fin, the lower lobe of the caudal fin, the pectoral fins and, to a variable extent, the other fin tips. (Black markings occur on the second dorsal fin and anal fin of smaller individuals.) The oceanic whitetip is often accompanied by pilotfishes (*Naucrates ductor*) – sometimes several dozen can be seen with a single shark.
DISTRIBUTION:	An oceanic shark of tropical to warm-temperate waters worldwide. Possibly present in the western Mediterranean, having entered from the Atlantic.
SIZE:	Attains over 3 metres but most individuals encountered are around 2 metres in length.

HABITAT:	This is a truly oceanic shark and is more common the further one goes from land. It favours the surface layers of the ocean. The oceanic whitetip is by no means uncommon in the Red Sea and is regularly encountered off open-water islands such as The Brothers. It is also occasionally seen off deep-water coastal reefs.
DIET:	It feeds on a wide variety of open-water fishes and cephalopods, although how such an apparently sluggish shark can occur in such numbers in the virtually empty wastes of the open ocean is something of a mystery. It has been suggested that the white markings act as a lure to bring open-water fishes in close. The fact that oceanic whitetips hang off open-water reefs suggests that they also feed on reef creatures.
COMMENTS:	The oceanic whitetip is a bold shark as is readily testified by anyone who has been in the water with one. It will swim up to investigate a diver and sometimes bump him with its snout. It then circles before another approach. It is not easily deterred in this activity: the circles become smaller, the bumps more determined – hence the need to be able to leave the water rapidly.

GREY REEF SHARK
Carcharhinus amblyrhynchos

IDENTIFICATION: The Red Sea variety of grey reef shark can be identified by a combination of two characteristics: the white marking on the apex of the first dorsal fin and the pronounced black edge to the caudal fin. (The second dorsal and anal fins are also edged in black.) Confusion exists over both the scientific and the common names of this shark (see Introduction). The alternative scientific name *Carcharhinus wheeleri* and common name blacktail shark are still current, although falling into disuse.

DISTRIBUTION: From the Red Sea to the Central Pacific.

SIZE: Rarely over 1.5 metres, although larger individuals are occasionally encountered. Maximum size is about 2 metres.

HABITAT: This is a very common shark of healthy Red Sea coral reefs, although it does seem to prefer reefs that drop into deep water to shallow, coastal ones. Many individuals can gather on the current-bathed promontories of such reefs.

DIET: The grey reef shark feeds on a wide variety of reef fishes, squid and octopuses. While the whitetip reef shark specializes in catching creatures hidden in the coral, the grey reef shark is more adept at feeding on free-swimming creatures.

COMMENTS: The grey reef shark is often seen during daytime swimming with trance-like disinterest on the deeper part of the reef. At dusk it can start feeding and become agitated and hostile to any diver in its area. It also occurs in open water where it can assume the aggressiveness of an open-water shark.

WHALE SHARK

Rhincodon typus

IDENTIFICATION: The whale shark is covered in white spots. Its size alone (usually over 4 metres in length) makes identification easy.

DISTRIBUTION: Occurs in warm waters throughout the world but is absent from the Mediterranean.

SIZE: Maximum size around 12 metres though there are reports of even larger ones.

HABITAT: The whale shark can be seen just about anywhere, from shallow water to open sea. During March and April as the water warms up and there is a plankton bloom, whale sharks are regularly seen on the Sinai reefs of Egypt and also on Yemeni reefs.

DIET: Feeds mainly on animal plankton (zooplankton) although it does eat small fishes.

COMMENTS: The whale shark can be curious and swim up to a diver for a close look, provided he or she is swimming calmly (not always easy when one of these huge animals puts in an appearance). Some divers grab hold of the shark and hitch a ride, which is unfortunate as the whale shark will then probably dive and not return.

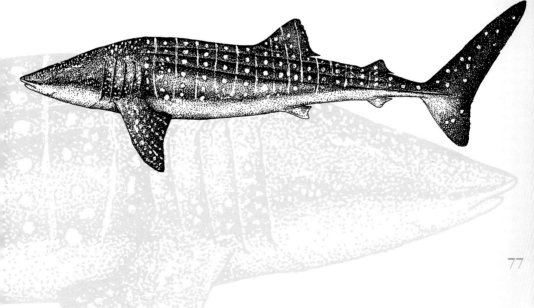

TIGER SHARK

Galeocerdo cuvier

IDENTIFICATION:	Juveniles are covered in a series of dark spots and dashes. These change into vertical dark stripes on the bodies of larger individuals, hence the common name. In large individuals (over about 4 metres) the stripes can fade. The head is massive and blunt-snouted, the mouth enormous and the eyes large and dark. The first dorsal fin is very broad-based and the body somewhat skinny behind it.
DISTRIBUTION:	Global distribution in tropical and temperate seas but not recorded from the Mediterranean.
SIZE:	Attains at least 5 metres, possibly considerably more.
HABITAT:	A roaming shark that can occur anywhere from open sea to inshore lagoon areas. Probably abundant in the Red Sea but rarely seen because of its tendency to swim at depths of several hundred metres during the day. The tiger shark will enter shallower water at night to hunt, and is sometimes seen apparently dozing on the surface.
DIET:	It has perhaps the most wide-ranging diet of all sharks and eats bony fishes, sharks, rays, crustaceans, cephalopods, sea turtles, sea birds, sea snakes (where they occur) and many apparently inedible things.
COMMENTS:	The tiger shark is known to be a man-eater. When encountered on a dive it is normally seen swimming by with complete disinterest. I have had a tiger shark swim right up to me when I was cutting up a barracuda for a shark feed on Sanganeb Reef in the Sudan. But it then turned and swam away without reappearing. There is at least one case where a tiger shark has followed a boat of divers who left one area to get away from it. It reappeared in their new dive location shortly after they re-entered the water – so they left again.

VARIEGATED SHARK

Stegostoma varium

IDENTIFICATION:	Adults are covered in dark spots, which is why some divers call it a leopard shark. Juveniles have a series of dark-edged white stripes and other divers call it a zebra shark. The caudal fin is enormous – about half the total length of the body. Only thresher sharks have equivalently elongated caudal fins. The snout is bulbous and rounded. There are nasal barbels.
DISTRIBUTION:	From the Red Sea and East African coast to New Caledonia and Palau.
SIZE:	Probably attains more than 3 metres, although most that have been seen were nearer 2 metres long.
HABITAT:	Being nocturnal it is usually seen during the day lying on the sandy bottom between coral heads. It tends to swim away sluggishly when approached.
DIET:	Feeds on shrimps, crabs, crayfishes, molluscs and bony fishes.
COMMENTS:	The variegated shark is fairly common on coastal reefs in the northern Red Sea. It seems to be particularly fond of channels into the lagoons of reefs and several variegated sharks can be encountered together in such areas.

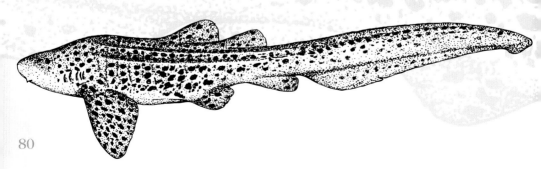

SILKY SHARK
Carcharhinus falciformis

IDENTIFICATION: The silky shark has a relatively long and thin body. The snout, when viewed from the side, is markedly pointed. The eyes are small. The first dorsal fin is relatively low and the apex is usually more rounded than pointed. The rear edge of the first dorsal fin can be undercut, making the fin slant backwards. When viewing a silky shark side on, if one draws an imaginary line straight down the body from the front point of origin of the first dorsal fin, the line will reach the belly well behind the rear inner corner of the pectoral fin. This is a useful identification tool. The second dorsal fin is very low and has a very long free rear tip.

DISTRIBUTION: In tropical and subtropical waters worldwide. Absent from the Mediterranean.

SIZE: Attains over 3 metres.

HABITAT: An open-water shark often encountered with marine mammals. It appears to be less oceanic than the oceanic whitetip; it is more common within reasonable distance of land. The silky will sometimes put in an appearance on deep-water reefs and sometimes several sharks will appear at once.

DIET: This is a swift and agile predator that feeds mainly on open-water fishes.

COMMENTS: The tendency of the silky to approach a diver boldly and repeatedly marks it as potentially dangerous. Divers have had to abort night dives on coral reefs because of its unwanted attentions.

DIET: The triangular, serrated teeth indicate that this shark feeds on a wide variety of food items including animals too large to swallow whole. It is known to specialize in feeding on stingrays. One has been observed first immobilizing a stingray by biting off its pectoral wing tips. A great hammerhead can often have numerous stingray barbs embedded in its head.

COMMENTS: The great hammerhead is occasionally seen from shore, hunting rays or bony fishes in shallow water. The spectacular commotion occasioned by a hunting great hammerhead demonstrates its immense power and agility. The occasional report of a very large, solitary hammerhead making a fearless close approach to divers on inshore reefs is suggestive of the great hammerhead. There is a report of a great hammerhead of some 4 metres in length appearing at Sanganeb Reef accompanied by numerous pilotfishes, which suggests that it was a recent arrival from an extended open-water voyage. The great hammerhead must be considered highly dangerous.

93

Date	Location	Depth	Sharks Observed

Date	Location	Depth	Sharks Observed
. . . .	. . . .	. . . .	. . . .
. . . .	. . . .	. . . .	. . . .
. . . .	. . . .	. . . .	. . . .
. . . .	. . . .	. . . .	. . . .
. . . .	. . . .	. . . .	. . . .
. . . .	. . . .	. . . .	. . . .
. . . .	. . . .	. . . .	. . . .
. . . .	. . . .	. . . .	. . . .
. . . .	. . . .	. . . .	. . . .
. . . .	. . . .	. . . .	. . . .
. . . .	. . . .	. . . .	. . . .
. . . .	. . . .	. . . .	. . . .
. . . .	. . . .	. . . .	. . . .
. . . .	. . . .	. . . .	. . . .
. . . .	. . . .	. . . .	. . . .

The Shark Trust

Established in 1997, the Shark Trust promotes the study, management and conservation of sharks, skates and rays.

The Shark Trust is calling for:
- sustainably managed shark fisheries
- reduced shark bycatch in other fisheries
- legal protection for threatened species
- conservation of breeding and nursery habitats
- increased research into shark biology and ecology
- development of national and international management and conservation strategies
- international conservation and research initiatives, including tag and release programmes
- increased public awareness of the conservation needs of these vulnerable animals

Please help to Save Our Sharks
Join now to receive your supporter pack, free shark poster and regular newsletters.
Adopt a shark, and support your choice of research and conservation projects around the world.

The Shark Trust
36 Kingfisher Court, Hambridge Road, Newbury, Berkshire, RG14 5SJ, UK.
Tel: (+44) 01635 551150.
Fax: (+44) 01635 550230.
E-mail: sharktrust@naturebureau.co.uk
Registered Charity No. 1064185.